SHOW ME
HAPPY

To my grandson, Lucas, whose smile
inspired this book—K.M.A.

To Laura and all our kids—E.F.

Thank you to all the families who graciously gave their time
to be photographed for this book—K.M.A. and E.F.

ISBN 978-0-545-90597-8

12 11 10 9 8 7 6 5 4 3 2 1   15 16 17 18 19 20/0

Printed in the U.S.A.   40

First Scholastic printing, September 2015

The design is by Jordan Kost.

SHOW ME
HAPPY

Kathryn Madeline Allen   photographs by Eric Futran

SCHOLASTIC INC.

Show me happy,

show me helping,

show me up,

show me down.

Show me holding,

show me giving,

show me hiding,

show me found.

Show me pushing,

show me pulling,

show me sharing when we play.

Show me NOISY,

show me quiet,

show me putting things away.

Show me little,

show me BIG,

show me one

and show me ten.

Now, with some kisses...

and some hugs...

let's show we're happy
to be friends.